Kara,

This is DEPRESSION

Yours in good health.

[signature]

R. AVERY BURTON

Rushmore Press LLC
www.rushmorepress.com
1 888 733 9607

This is Depression

ISBN   Softcover   978-1-7328613-0-5

Printed in the United States of America.

CONTENTS

INTRODUCTION

I am a storyteller. Usually, my stories are about someone else - clients or colleagues. However, this time I'm writing about the events that led me to become an advocate for mental health and depression.

First, let me take you back to the early 80s. I remember sitting in class at Crozier Junior High School in Inglewood, California and someone slowly entered the classroom and handed the teacher a note. I had been summoned to the front office where my family picked me up early from school.

My dad and three siblings were all quiet as I got into the car. Almost like they were protecting me from something. They were. My mom had passed away. I was 13 years old.

My mom had been sick, but I had no idea how bad it was until the doctors were trying to explain how this little-known disease called Lupus caused her death. All I knew was that my mother was gone.

This was my first brush with losing a close relative. I was confused and numb. I was a straight up mammas boy. Nothing could replace her, but I recall how my family did their best to fill the gaping whole in my life. How my sisters would take me school shopping in exchange for watching soap operas. How my brother would now let me touch his stuff, like his prized comic book collection.

How my dad, bad back and all from working 20 plus years at Firestone Tire and Rubber, became Mr. Mom, raising me with tough love and a mother's concern.

There was the time that year when I dedicated one of my basketball games to my mom, floating through the YMCA gym, my sneakers never touching the ground as I scored the most points I ever had in a game.

What I don't remember is meeting with a grief counselor. No appointments with a therapist to learn how to process the feelings of losing the person who brought me into this world, never got a chance to see me graduate from high school, go to college, get married and have kids.

All I can remember is how important it was to have my family to lean on and to help ease the pain I felt inside. Growing up in Inglewood, a suburb of Los Angeles, I lived in a middle-class neighborhood in an urban environment that would be the backdrop to Laker's championship parades, portrayed in movies and hip-hop songs.

Growing up, I guess you could say I had seen and heard a lot of things.

In high school, you would hear about a friend getting shot and killed over the weekend. Or there was the night I got a ride home from a co-worker at the recreation center where I worked. Her car was on empty, so I ran into my backyard and got a gas can we used for the lawn mower and began pouring it into the tank as we talked.

Then a car drives by slowly and we watched as the red brake lights turned to white, as the car reversed and a thin shadowy figure gets out.

A question was asked and a response was given. I guess I must have given the right response because the guy got back in the car and drove away. Or maybe as they say, it was not my time to go.

I carried these experiences and others with me into adulthood and they helped shaped me as a husband and parent.

Despite a few childhood memories of loss and close calls, not once did I seriously think about having to bury one of my kids.

Then in 2017, my son passed away.

His death was the result of an illness that afflicts people of all ages and backgrounds, but is particularly harmful to students: he had a major depressive episode.

The cause of his death was hidden in my parental blind spot. By sharing his story, I am hoping that others can learn from my experiences.

Avery Burton was a confident, physically fit, ambitious 22-year with a loving family life and lots of friends. He had recently graduated from college and had plans to pursue a doctoral degree in physical therapy.

On July 24, a little over two months after his college graduation he took his life by jumping from a bridge at Hoover Dam, about a 20-minute drive from our house in Henderson, Nevada.

To this day, it's still hard to believe he is no longer with us. As my dentist told me during a recent visit and who also treated my son:

"If you offered me a million dollars and asked me which of my patients I thought might be struggling, he (Avery) would have not made the list. I still can't believe it," he told me.

Just like after my mom passed away, I was stunned and confused.

What was a depressive episode?

How does someone go from celebrating a lifelong achievement to stress to suicidal thoughts in just over two months?

As it turns out, Avery was not alone in his struggle with mental health and depression. I was stunned to learn:

- 1 in 4 college students suffers from depression.
- 1 in 7 males suffers from depression
- The suicide rate among young adults, ages 15-24, has tripled since the 1950s and suicide is the most common cause of death among college students
- 1,100: number of suicides that occur at colleges every year – 7.5 per 100,000 students

According to a PBS report on teen suicide and schools, the Centers for Disease Control and Prevention lists suicide as now the second-leading cause of death for ages 10 to 18, and the number of teens reporting feeling sad, hopeless or suicidal has risen. But experts say suicide is preventable.

I thought depression was something that happened to people from dysfunctional families or backgrounds.

My wife and I didn't do drugs or drink excessively. Sure, we argued from time to time, but tried not to in front of the kids. We both worked hard to give our three boys a chance at a good life, in a safe neighborhood with great schools.

In the end, none of that mattered. My son hid his depression from our family.

There were a few signs. He had spoken about how stressful his life had become after graduation.

What should have been a time of joy had become joyless. He confided in a few friends about having suicidal thoughts.

By the time the word got to us, we were not sure what to do and things were escalating quickly.

So we did what we had always done. We held him close, made sure he knew he was not alone, that we would get through whatever he was dealing with together as a family like we always had.

Took him on vacation. Surrounded him with family and love. Hoping he was snap out of his funk. Sure, he was driven and could be hard on himself, but I would answer the question my dentist posed the same way.

But I was wrong. Love is not enough. Not when it comes to depression. I was wrong to think mental health issues and depression was something *others* had to deal with.

Maybe I was naïve, but I didn't know Avery was sick or that his illness would cause him to take his own life.

Depression robbed him of his confidence and optimism. He no longer saw the bright future that everyone else envisioned. His world was now dark and upside down. Where others saw a leader, he looked in the mirror and saw someone unworthy of praise or the ability to lead.

He could no longer envision the bright future that led him to proudly pose in pictures in medical scrubs or title a snap chat, "Call me Dr. Burton."

At this point, I know what you must be thinking. This is another book written by a grieving parent, seeking healing and sympathy in the aftermath of loss.

If that's the case, then you can skip to Chapter's 6 and 7 to find the source of my spiritual healing.

I wrote this book to help educate people about a serious illness. To add my voice to a much-needed conversation about mental health and depression.

But first, I needed to provide the backstory on the minds family and friends: what happened to Avery.

If you choose to read on, you will learn that the struggle with mental illness is real and it doesn't discriminate.

My grieving and healing process would have to wait. There were too many things to do. A memorial service to plan.

A program to write and get published. Most importantly, I had a wife who lost her first son to comfort. I had two boys, ages 20 and 15 who had just lost their big brother in the most unimaginable way, to lift up.

There was also a host of family, friends and confused people who lost a grandson, nephew, cousin, a friend, someone they looked up to.

High school and university staff and professors trying to understand how and why a student, a regular on their Dean's list who had just graduated from college cum laude could not see his bright future was worth living for.

Putting my bereavement process on hold, I decided to write a book about my experience.

By opening up and sharing my story from the most painful period of my life, my hope was to not let his passing be in vain.

To help other parents and families, potentially saving lives. To bring awareness to depression and mental health issues.

To add my voice to the conversation, in the hopes that others may find theirs.

But first, we needed answers. Without them, how could we survive?

CHAPTER 1

This is Depression

On the surface, July 24th, 2017 was like any other summer day at our house. The laughter of the boys playing video games or the sounds of the washing machine humming usually filled the air. My wife Ann and I were happy to have each of our three boys home together for another few weeks before they headed back to school.

Beneath the surface, concerns about our oldest son Avery were coming to a head.

It was her day off, so she took the boys to eat lunch, run errands including a stop at Costco to get passport photos for the boys. Just to have them ready, maybe for that trip to the Philippines, we had been putting off for what seemed like years. I was working then came home to change clothes for a business networking function later that evening.

I got a call on my cell around 6 pm as I was driving in Downtown along Las Vegas Boulevard, five minutes away from a networking event.

It was my 20-year-old son Amani.

Like most millennial kids, he never calls and usually texts. That was the first sign something was wrong.

"Did you see the text from Kuya in our group chat?," I replied, "No, I'm driving". He replied flatly, you should read it. I said hold on and I immediately pulled the car over on the side of a downtown street.

I scrolled through my texts until I found the one from Kuya. "I'm so sorry, but this had to be done. I love you, Team Burton."

Kuya is Avery Burton, my 22-year old son. It means Big Brother in Filipino.

The next thing I heard was Amani's voice still on the phone. "You need to read the post on his Facebook Page."

I said, "alright, let me call you right back." I opened the Facebook app on my phone and found the post. The words jumped through the screen on my cell phone and pierced my heart.

It started: "The first thing everyone needs to know, is that it's nobody's fault. This needed to be done."

That's when it hit me. He was gone. Earlier in the day, he had driven from our home in Henderson to Hoover Dam, which is about a 20 to 25-minute drive. He parked just inside the security stop. Hiked a short distance to the bridge that connects Nevada and Arizona. Changed his mind and came back home.

"The marijuana saved me, lol", he texted to a friend earlier.

The same friend texted me, and I mentioned it to Ann and we both agreed to talk with him that night. He told friends he had made an appointment to see a counselor. At no time did we think he was a danger to himself or anyone else.

Before leaving for work, I asked Avery if we could drop Amani at the airport on Monday. That was three days away. He response gave me confidence that he wasn't going to do anything drastic.

"No problem, I got him," he replied without hesitation.

Avery hid his depression from us. He didn't was his family to know he we were struggling emotionally, especially Ann and I.

Still, I was hoping there was a one percent chance I was wrong and the need to stay strong for my wife Ann and the boys. I called Amani back and told him to try and reach someone in The Squad, his tight-knit group of friends from the University of Nevada Las Vegas.

I hung up and called the Boulder City Police Department, the closest one to the Hoover Dam. I reported Avery missing, gave them a description of the car – a black 2001 Hyundai Santa Fe SUV. I gave him the car when he got his license for the junior year of high school. The paint was fading and the AC stopped working his freshman year of college, but he loved "Frank", his nickname for the car.

I told them he was at Hoover Dam and that's where they would likely find him. I told them I was on my way there.

The dispatch said no Mr. Burton, go home and wait for the Henderson Police Department, a quiet family-friendly city 10 minutes Southeast of the Las Vegas Strip where we had lived for 17 years.

By the time I got home, two of his closest friends were already there. Several other friends had driven to Hoover Dam to try and find Avery.

Jeff Henderson, a colleague and close family friend saw Avery's post on Facebook and called my cell. We had worked together years earlier at MGM Mirage.

"You need me to come thru homey?" Boomed the voice on the other end.

I said "yes" hung up and walked into the house. The police were already there to get a statement. I tried to be strong for Ann and the boys. Maybe the pressure of school was too much and he needed a break to clear his head, I theorized.

After waiting for a few hours, we got a call from the Boulder City area police. They asked us to come to Hoover Dam. Jeff goes by Chef Jeff, a celebrity chef who had been on The Food Network and several reality TV shows. He had a large van he used when he traveled for cooking shows, so we all jumped into the van and drove to Hoover Dam.

The first thing I noticed when we got there was the body language of the police and Lake Mead officials. It was not good. They took us to his car, where it was parked alone. His wallet and gym bag were in the car.

According to the police report and eyewitness statement, this time, there would be no second thoughts. He parked his car and left the keys. Sent the group chat and Facebook post from his I-Phone, sat the phone on the rail and climbed over the fence, 1,000 feet over the Colorado River. Witnesses say they saw a physically fit and well developed, black male climb on the bridge railing.

I grabbed Ann and the boys in a group hug. It was finally starting to set in. Avery was gone. Tears began to flow from everyone. I looked around and his friends stood there in disbelief. Chef Jeff gave us space, but as a parent, I could see the hurt on his face as he just shook his head. The phone calls, texts and Facebook messages started to pour in.

All we could do was go home and wait for the official outcome that wouldn't come for weeks. With everyone still in a state of shock, Ann and I didn't say much to the boys. Avery loved the outdoors – hiking, cliff diving, camping. Privately, I think we hoped he went on a trip. Needed some time to clear his mind.

It was during these moments, I knew I had to try and be strong and find the answers to the question everyone – family, friends, classmates, professors wanted to know – what happened.

CHAPTER 2

Team Burton

When we moved to Las Vegas to work for a large hotel and casino company on the Las Vegas Strip in early 2000, it was a good move professionally. For anyone working in the hospitality industry, Las Vegas was the big leagues. A lot of my colleagues were happy for me.

With some family and friends, the reaction was a little different. "How are you going to raise a family in Las Vegas" was something we heard from more than a few.

My response was simple: *"Parents raise kids, not cities."*

Like most parents, we wanted the best we could offer for the boys. So I asked my realtor for a listing of the places with the best schools and area to raise a family. He said either Summerlin, a master-planned community about 15 minutes west of the Las Vegas Strip or Green Valley, a master planned community in Henderson, about 15 minutes Southeast on the opposite side of town.

I only wanted listings in Henderson. I liked the small, family-friendly feel with lots of parks and trails.

We never talked much about it, but Ann and I always felt like we had to be the luckiest parents in Nevada or anywhere. Raising three boys is hard work, but our boys made us proud and kept things fun at home.

R. Avery Burton

Ann is Filipina and from a close-knit family. She had a bit of the Asian Tiger Mom thing going, too. Made sure the boys had whatever they needed. The meals, stuff for school, music instruments – she made it all happen.

I was a Mini Van Dad, enjoyed driving the boys to the practices, games and hanging out with the dads occasionally on the weekends or end of season parties.

Our family vacations were either to visit the in-laws or combined trips with visiting college campuses. Nevada ranks amongst the lowest states in education, especially drop out rates.

We wanted to make sure the boys knew the expectation was that they were going to college. Ann trusted me to help with academics and the father-son stuff. We stayed in our lanes.

I would tell my friends I stopped doing homework by the time they were all in middle school. I focused on trying to prepare them for life. Everything was going as planned.

In the summer of 2017, Avery had just graduated from the University of Nevada Las Vegas with a degree in kinesiological sciences and was taking a semester off to work and put together his graduate school application for UNLV Physical Therapy School in December.

It was a doctoral program and he knew it would not be easy, but he was 22 years old, passed the GRE on the first try and wanted to be a physical therapist.

All his hard work had paid off up until this point.

Amani, 19, was visiting from Tempe and a month away from beginning his junior year at Barrett, The Honors College at Arizona State University, where he was a business major. Amani was my business guy, took pride in making good grades and always thinking about ways to make money. Then there was Aden, our 14-year old who was about to start his freshman year at Coronado High School in Henderson.

Like his brothers, Aden was good in school, was the only one accepted into the Gifted and Talented Education Program (GATE) for students who need a bit more of a challenge in elementary school. He took full advantage of being the Bunso, which is the youngest or baby of the family in Filipino. He ran our house.

All three boys excelled in academics and athletics but Avery was the leader and set the bar high.

Everyone loved Avery

Growing up, Avery was shy and a bit of an introvert. I remember when he 4 or 5, he signed with Ford Models For Kids, a Beverly Hills modeling agency. It was a big deal to everyone but him. We drove him to photo shoots in and around LA and the photographers had a hard time getting him to smile.

If he didn't know you, he wasn't going to smile. So after a few longer than usual shoots, they stopped calling him back. Unlike most parents, we didn't want to force him into it, so we pulled him out. We kept his checks and never cashed them.

As he got older he became more confident and grew out of his shyness. A three-sport athlete at Foothill High, he wasn't the tallest or most physically imposing kid growing up, but nobody worked harder. He had the work ethic coaches loved and teammates respected, earning the prestigious White Letter for lettering in three varsity sports in the same year.

Our family was a fixture at FHS tennis, wrestling and track and field practices and events. I don't remember whose idea it was, but Ann had t-shirts made up that read: Team Burton. We wanted Avery to know we were there to watch and support him.

Avery had natural leadership ability. He was not a talkative or "rah rah" guy. He was a leader by example with a bright smile that took over a room. It was not surprising that he was the starter on the 4x2 relay team that set the school record.

He was the starter, the person responsible for passing the baton first and made sure his team got off to a good start.

He had a unique combination of smarts and passion for fitness. I referred to him as "Intellectual Brutality." He earned a degree in kinesiology at UNLV, graduating cum laude while working as a lifeguard and licensed personal trainer in the campus recreational center.

He loved brainteasers, so he learned algorithms for the Rubik's cube and would do them over and over on family vacations. Other kids would interrupt our dinner at restaurants to watch him match up all the colors in record time.

He would get bored easily, so to keep his mind sharp he taught himself how to play chess. First on his phone, then when he got good enough, he bought a chess set and played against his co-workers at the pool.

"Everyone looked up to him because he was smart and he was always there to provide motivation," his friends would say.

****

Early in my professional career, I was looking to leave the journalism business. I was a living and working for a newspaper in Reno, Nevada, the Reno Gazette-Journal and like most young reporters, I was getting restless and asking myself when was I going to get the opportunity to work at my hometown newspaper, the LA Times or get that big promotion to USA Today.

One day I got a call from a friend and colleague, Dr. Paul Mitchell, who is now a dean at the University of Nevada Reno. He told me about an opening in the public relations department of the Los Angeles Rams and San Diego Chargers and encouraged me to apply. The Rams had announced a move to St. Louis, and well, being from Southern California, San Diego sounded more appealing so I sent my resume and cover letter to Bill Johnston, who then was the Director of Public Relations for the Chargers. Ironically, at the time of writing this book, both teams have since moved to Los Angeles where they will play in a brand new stadium in my hometown of Inglewood.

I interviewed and they agreed to bring me in for Training Camp to see if I could handle the NFL grind. I had worked in my sports information department for Lawrence Fan in college at San Jose State, so I felt prepared. I somehow survived a grueling summer of practices, travel and media assignments to get the job. We made it to the Super Bowl that year. During the season, Avery was born while I was in New Orleans for our game against the Saints. I flew back after the game to San Diego with the team and booked a flight to Reno to be with him and Ann. They both moved down to San Diego after the season. Soon, Avery was a fixture at home games in Jack Murphy Stadium sitting in one of the suites and roaming the bleachers as soon as he could walk.

So I guess you could say Avery was destined to be involved in sports. Like most kids, he played all the youth sports growing up, but we enjoyed the family atmosphere of the Henderson Flag Football League the most.

As he got older, Avery became more interested in working out and nutrition, so I took him to see a sports nutritionist the summer before high school to talk about weight gain, sport specific training, and protein intake. He loved every aspect of sports training. Before long we were mixing our own special brand of Gatorade designed for endurance for the long hot days in late summer on the tennis court. This was the beginning of his passion for health and fitness.

By the time he got to high school, Avery had quit football but he had grown into an athlete who was always looking to challenge himself in school and sports.

Now a college graduate, armed with a part-time job at a Henderson physical therapy office, good family life, a healthy social life and plans to apply to the Physical Therapy Program at UNLV to pursue a doctoral degree, the future looked bright for the kid who once sent a snap chat to friends that read, "Call Me Dr. Burton."

With the biggest challenges still ahead, as far as we could tell, the struggles started right after college graduation on May 13, 2017.

CHAPTER 3

First Signs of Trouble

When I was in college studying journalism at San Jose State, I landed a summer internship at the Riverside Press-Enterprise, about an hour east of LA.

I got a chance to cover a junior golf tournament. It was one of the few sports I didn't play and I was not a huge fan. However, there was a young teenager that was making some noise that I wanted to write about.

His name was Eldrick Woods but soon the world would call him by his nickname, Tiger.

Aside from watching him play, I was struck by something else. It was how Woods handled the media and pressure of playing one of the most difficult sports.

One of the more memorable quotes from the tournament came when a reporter asked him what he hoped to accomplish in a pro career.

Woods replied confidently, "I want to be the Michael Jordan of golf."

The quote revealed not only confidence, but was the equivalent of trash talk in golf.

Woods went on to win the tournament and eventually turned professional. I later discovered that he had been working with a sports psychologist to help sharpen his mental approach to the sport.

That experience of covering Woods would come back to help me years later.

When Avery started high school and wanted to try out for the tennis team, I was all for it. Although he had never picked up a racket, I had played in high school and offered to train him. He was already a good athlete, so I had all summer before his freshman year to get him ready for tryouts.

He picked up the sport quickly but due to his inexperience, he lacked the confidence you need in a sport like tennis, where 90% percent of the game is played above the shoulders.

Avery made the varsity team his freshman year at Foothill High School, largely because he was one of the fastest kids in school and easily ran under the time necessary to complete the mile run given to each player.

But he still had much to learn to be competitive and help the team. To give him an edge and help accelerate his learning curve, I got him the book, "The Inner Game of Tennis" by Tim Gallwey.

What impressed me is that despite the title, the book wasn't really about the sport of tennis. It concentrated on the fact that, as Gallwey wrote, *"Every game is composed of two parts, an outer game, and an inner game."*

The former is played against opponents, he wrote, and is filled with lots of contradictory advice; the latter is played not against, but within the mind of the player, and its principal obstacles are self-doubt and anxiety.

Gallwey's revolutionary thinking, built on a foundation of Zen philosophy and humanistic psychology, was really a primer on how to get out of your own way to let your best game emerge.

It wasn't his favorite sport, but Avery enjoyed the competition and took on the challenge of learning a new sport and succeeding against players who had been playing for years.

As I was writing this book I remembered this story. Looking back, it was probably the first and only time I proactively and somewhat indirectly, tried to help Avery with his mental health.

"Mommy, life is hard,"

After graduation in May 2017, I remembered we were all proud of Avery. Although he was on track to apply to graduate school and had a part-time job for the summer, he was feeling something different:

Stress.

"Mommy, life is hard," Ann remembered him telling her one-day after work at his job with a local physical therapy office.

Then there was a day less than a month after graduation where he came into my room one evening and sat on the floor in front of the closet as I sat on my bed working on my laptop. It was odd because the kids never came into the bedroom unless the other bathroom was being used.

"I don't know if grad school is for me," he started. My first thought was where is this coming from, but as a parent, I knew I needed to listen.

"I just don't think I have what it takes to be a PT or work in the medical profession," he went on to say. *"I don't feel like I have the people skills."*

The first thing that popped into my mind was that his confidence was gone, but the question was why?

I tried to remind him that he had done everything necessary to put himself in position to be accepted into a competitive program. That he would he would not only get accepted into the program but that he would probably be number one in his class.

That anything he feels he would be missing would be gained in a classroom or from being around other students pushing for the same goal.

Competition always brought out the best in him, so I thought by challenging him it would help.

I added that we as parents and a family could not be more proud of him. We would support him no matter what he wanted to do in life.

It was one of my better Dad son talks, but he stood up, walked away with a furry brow and sighed as he wandered down the hall and back into his room.

The next day, I texted him and asked how he was doing.

I got a text back immediately:

"You are right. I did put myself in a good position. I think I was just freaking out!"

While I thought the problem had been solved or at least averted, the stress was slowly building and stirring deeper inside his mind and body.

The pressure cooker inside him started to boil around the 4th of July. He had just got back from camping with friends and canceled on watching fireworks with the family. He was too tired from the trip and would rather sleep.

A few weeks later, I got the text from one of his best friends.

"I heard from a friend that Avery has been talking about suicide. I needed to tell you," said the voice on the other end of the phone.

Needless to say, I was concerned.

"Please don't tell him I told you. He doesn't want you guys to know." I said okay, thanks and hung up.

I immediately told Ann. We wondered what we should do. Should we talk to him?

Would that make things worse?

"We are planning a vacation, let's take the boys to LA and visit our families," we both thought.

"Maybe getting away will help ease his mind."

So we visited my in-laws in North Hollywood, my brother and sister in Hawthorne and my other sister in Carson. And of course, the highlight of the trip was a visit to the ocean in Manhattan Beach.

When we returned home he seemed fine. He still had his trademark sense of humor, texting me ideas for a press release I was doing for a client. A popular international Filipino restaurant.

"You can always describe the sauce as a lotion to make it more appealing. Who wouldn't love a good knuckle sandwich," he texted with crying laughing emojis in response to my struggle to describe Crispy Pata, a popular Filipino dish of pig knuckles.

The vacation did little to quiet his mind and his struggles came to a head on July 24.

The calls and text messages came right away. Condolences from relatives, friends, classmates, and neighbors poured in. The food deliveries to our house from families and colleagues to were non-stop. His memorial service on August 21 was standing room only. They had to open the overflow room to accommodate everyone.

We decided to show the service on Facebook Live for family and friends who could not make it but wanted to pay their respects.

****

According to our grief counselors at UNLV, they believe Avery had a Major Depressive Episode or MDE brought on by the indecision of career path after graduation.

The handout the therapists provided during one session outlined the Diagnostic Criteria for MDE, which includes five or more of the following symptoms.

1. *Depressed mood most of the day, nearly every day*
2. *Markedly diminished interest in pleasure in all, or almost all, activities most of the day nearly every day*
3. *Significant weight loss when not dieting or weight gain*
4. *Insomnia or hypersomnia nearly every day*
5. *Psychomotor agitation or retardation nearly every day*
6. *Fatigue*
7. *Feelings of worthlessness or excessive or inappropriate guilt*
8. *Diminished ability to think or concentrate or indecisiveness*
9. *Recurrent thoughts of death or a specific plan for committing suicide*

Looking back, Avery had at least five of the symptoms.

He began to withdraw from his friends. The kid I teased as the Black Baywatch in his lifeguard uniform showing off his muscular and sinewy body suddenly didn't want to work out. The most disciplined person I have ever met who loved his bed was getting poor or little to no sleep. The overachiever who hardly sat still suddenly couldn't move to take his dirty clothes down the hall to the laundry room.

The loss of weight had to be normal stress or his stomach problems, right?

How did we miss the signs?

How did things go from stress to depression seemingly so quickly?

Couldn't we or shouldn't we have done more?

This had to be our fault, right? I kept thinking.

Despite the internal pain brought on by his depressive episode, Avery provided us with the answers to most of our questions.

It was almost like he wanted us to know what happened, for our healing and to help others. The clues were rooted in his final post on Facebook and text messages to friends he left on his phone.

CHAPTER 4

A Message For Family and Friends

A very posted his suicide note on Facebook. While it provided some answers, I imagined that it also created some confusion for people that he might not have spoken to or been in close contact with other than social media.

In this chapter, I try to clear a few things up and offer some context.

As someone who works in communications, I knew I had to draft a statement from the family to address the Facebook post and what happened.

The first line is his post read:

"The first thing everyone should know is that it's nobody's fault."

One of the first things we covered in grief counseling was the idea of seeking blame for the actions of the person that has passed away from suicide. It's a natural reaction.

Avery knew we would blame ourselves. Ann felt guilty that she didn't try and keep him at home that day.

His friends wondered what if anything they said or did that pushed him over the edge. I even asked myself should I have forced him into counseling.

The truth?

He made a unilateral decision for himself. It was nothing anyone said or did. There was nothing anyone could have said or done. He had made up his mind and once he did, the combination of a lack of sleep and the subconscious made him impulsive.

As is the case with people having a depressive episode, it was only a matter of time before the impulse to end the pain would take over.

"I was living a Fake Life"

Avery was looking forward to life after college following his graduation in May, including applying to PT school in December. He finished the semester with a 3.8 GPA, passed his GRE exam on the first try and had already lined up a PT tech job in 7 Hills part-time, not far from our house. He was ready for a much-needed break from school.

After graduation, he mentioned that he was started to have second thoughts about graduate school. That he didn't feel prepared for such a big step.

Clearly, he was stressing out a bit over big life decisions. We encouraged him to stick to the plan laid out four years ago. He agreed.

Over the next few weeks, we noticed he was losing weight and not eating much due to stomach problems, which were normal for him. Again, we chalked it up to stress and told him we would support whatever he wanted to do, that he was a college graduate with a bright future.

One of the most surreal moments in our healing was getting mail from UNLV. It was Avery's diploma. He graduated with honors, cum laude.

The idea of Avery living a "Fake Life" was difficult to wrap my mind around. He had a great family life, lots of friends, well respected by peers, was a good big brother and made us proud by making the Dean's List at UNLV the last two semesters.

Despite all the good stuff he had going on in his life, depression had turned his world upside down, altered his reality.

"I was unhappy before the drugs and PT Job"

During the 2016 election cycle, my firm was selected to manage statewide communications for the Campaign to Regulate Marijuana Like Alcohol (CMRLA), the ballot initiative to regulate recreational marijuana in Nevada. We had nationally tested messaging and data that we knew would help us win. To hear stories about veterans and families using medical marijuana, which was already legal in the state, were extremely compelling.

So when Avery referenced drugs, I knew exactly what that meant. He was self-medicating, using a certain strain of cannabis that helped him cope with "anxiety, emotions and feeling more alive" he wrote in a text to a friend.

I eventually learned from talking with his friends, he smoked marijuana to be more "social" and to stimulate his appetite (he had stomach problems) and to help relax and manage his stress.

One day I was in his room after he passed, looking for clues that might help me understand what happened to my son. In the desk drawer, I found a notebook for one of his classes. One particular assignment was a health assessment that measured the four conditions: mental, emotional, physical and environmental.

Avery scored below average one key area: emotional health. When the professor asked him what he thought about the score and ideas for improvement. He wrote:

"It's hard to fix a problem if you don't know one exists. I will work on it now that I know it needs fixing."

That was classic Avery. When healthy and not depressed, he was rational and not impulsive.

As for the part-time PT job, he described some issues with "ethics" in how the practice ran their business. It was clear he was not a fit, which was a bit of a surprise because he fit in every place he had worked.

"So much pain."

Regarding his comments about pain … we believe Avery suffered from physical and emotional pain brought on by his stomach problems, loss of appetite, weight loss and overall lack of energy and interest in being social.

One day while looking at his texts messages and on his Ipad, I found one very interesting. He texted a friend: *"I wish I could start over with a new brain and body."*

The stomach problems were so bad that he could not eat a meal in one sitting. So at dinner, he would sit down and start eating and suddenly disappear to his room. After everyone was done, we would clear the table except for his.

"Avery, are you done eating," one of us would yell.

"Nah, still working on it," he would reply.

So we would leave his plate on the table and sure enough he finished and put his plate in the sink. After a while, I think Ann or one of the boys gave him a nickname: Halftime.

As in, "where is Avery … is he done eating?" No, "he's at halftime."

"It's Hard When You Don't Have a Voice"

Avery had a great family life, with lots of friends in the neighborhood and school. He was a leader, but mostly by example. He was by no means the kind of student who talked just to stir things up. He voiced his opinion when it was required or he was asked to chime in on politics or current events. He stayed away from debates on social media because he was usually too busy to care what other people thought felt it was "pointless" to try and change their point of view.

When he felt it was necessary, he would raise his voice to stand up for himself.

When I read the words, my first thought was confusion. "It's hard when you don't have a voice" read the line in his Facebook post. What did he mean?

I believe what he meant by "it's hard when you don't have a voice" is that he had a hard time expressing his feelings in social environments. All of our boys are quiet, but he might be the shyest. He felt this was part of a pattern of not being good in social interactions required for working with patients.

Later on, after reading some of his texts and talking to his circle of friends, I also believe Avery was concerned about a slight stutter he had since he was in elementary school. The speech pathologist said he would eventually grow out of it. It got better but was still noticeable.

It presented two problems for him – one is the thought not having perfect speech might hurt his chances to get a job in a leadership position after college.

On a personal level, sometimes when he was out with friends, someone might ask what he wanted to eat and someone might answer for him. I think they may have felt they were doing him a favor so he didn't have to answer, especially in front of people he didn't know. He felt it was annoying and unnecessary but never raised the issue.

I'm not sure if he was made fun of or bullied about his speech, but I started to feel like that might also want he meant by it's hard when you don't have a voice.

"This had to be done"

On the outside, Avery must have appeared like the kid who could not miss. He worked his butt off in school, worked two jobs and had a healthy social life. He stayed busy and accomplished all of his goals. But on the inside, he was in turmoil. He was having doubts about his future.

Based on conversations with him and his friends over the final weeks of his life, it became clear that Avery suffered his depressive episode triggered by brought on by 1) He mutually left his PT job because it wasn't a "good fit"; 2) stress following graduation 3) obsessing about his career and life goals.

Everything escalated so fast. All we could do was still try and wrap our minds around what exactly happened. We appreciated and felt everyone's concern and sympathies but we had more questions than answers, which made it hard to talk about with our families.

The lack of sleep. The subconscious mind taking over. The feeling of doubt and worthlessness. It didn't take long before Avery began to succumb to the suicidal thoughts flowing through his mind. Between the self-medication with the cannabis and the alcohol acting as a depressant, Avery was vulnerable to making an impulsive decision.

I think this is what he meant by this had to be done. The depression had taken over his mind and he needed to stop the pain and anguish, one way or another. He didn't see himself getting better and did not want to be on antidepressants or using cannabis for the rest of his life just to feel normal.

CHAPTER 5

Healing After Loss

Grief fills the room up of my absent child,
Lies in his bed walks up and down with me,
Puts on his pretty looks, repeats his words,
Remembers me all of his gracious parts,
Stuffs out his vacant garments with his form.

- William Shakespeare

In 1985, I had just graduated from high school and enrolled at Santa Monica College where I discovered my interest in writing. That summer before school started and against my dad's wishes, I bought a rusted out 1970 Karman Ghia with some money I had saved up.

I had never even heard of the car, but I liked it. One of my buddies from the neighborhood had a Volkswagen Bug he restored. You could hear the sound of his modified muffler blocks away. He said he would help me fix it up.

After some primer, a $99 Earl Schieb paint job, and rebuilt engine, I was the proud owner of a hot pink Karman Ghia. I still remember the 30-minute drive to school on the 405 Freeway to the 10, catching looks the whole way.

One day I came out to the car after class and found a note from another student that read:

"My daddy will buy your car … call me."

Not long after I bought the car, a strange thing started happening. I began noticing more Karman Ghia's on the road all throughout LA. I had lived in Southern California my whole life and could not remember seeing one.

All of a sudden, no matter where I went, from Costa Mesa in Orange County to Santa Monica, I always saw a Karman Ghia.

Baader-Meinhof Phenomenon

At SMC, I remembered taking psychology class where this had been discussed. The experience would later be called the Baader-Meinhof phenomenon, but back then it was more commonly known as frequency illusion or recency illusion.

Basically, something you've just noticed, experienced or been told about suddenly crops up constantly. It gives you the feeling that out of nowhere this thing has engulfed you.

The reality is, the thing you are noticing has always been around – you're just noticing it more.

Major Depressive Disorder

That describes how I felt about becoming more aware of Major Depressive Disorder or depression. I was aware of issues related to mental health, depression and suicide but more on a professional level. Things you read in the newspaper, hear about on television or the radio.

I could not recall knowing anyone – family or friends, who had experienced issues related to depression or suicidal thoughts.

In fact, if you asked me for a list of the top 20 things I was worried about as a parent, depression was number 40. Way down on the list.

It just wasn't on my radar or occurred to me that it was a threat to the health of my family.

When I went out for a beer with the guys or other parents, it wasn't something we talked about.

All of a sudden, I was constantly starting to notice topics related to mental health and depression.

In the fall of 2017, the headline in the Las Vegas Review-Journal jumped out like a neon sign. UNLV announced it was increasing tuition for the fall semester by $25 to pay for more health counselors.

Why?

According to the article, students were waiting anywhere from four to six weeks for an appointment to see a therapist. I had no clue what the normal time should be, but I just knew that even if Avery had made an appointment through school to see a therapist, it would probably been too late.

Fortunately, the school realized that was too much time, especially in an environment where one in four students suffers from depression.

About a month later, I came across a story about UCLA offering free mental health screening for freshman and transfer students. This was the first time anything like that had been offered by the UC system.

A few weeks after Avery's memorial service, I was able to retrieve his phone from Las Vegas Metro Police Department. I took the phone home and charged the battery.

When the phone was back on, the Spotify app opened up. The last song Avery was listening too was "In the End" by the band Linkin Park. The lead singer, Chester Bennington had committed suicide a week before Avery.

As I was going back through some of Avery's social media posts, I noticed he liked a story about Bennington's death.

As I was writing this book, I continued to notice more and more headlines related to anxiety and depression.

Professional athletes were starting to open up and starred in Public Service Announcements about their struggles with anxiety. First, there was Olympic gold medal swimmer Michael Phelps. Then NBA stars Demar DeRozan and Kevin Love.

Of course, there were the highly publicized suicides of celebrities Kate Spade and Anthony Bourdain.

In some ways, I guess you could say I found some healing in knowing more about the mental health issue that led to my son's death.

Stigma of Depression

Despite the best intentions, I felt like society does not relate well to the problems of celebrities struggling in the "spotlight" and we tend to move on from the tragedy and back to the issues in our own lives.

I realized this after hearing story after story from family, friends and neighbors about their own struggles with mental health or one of their kids. I wondered how I could know someone for 5, 10, 15 years and the topic never came up.

Hearing these personal stories brought some healing from talking, but I knew more needed to be done to save our families and kids. That is why I am lending my voice to the conversation.

But first, I had to forgive myself. I often sat in Avery's room and replayed things over in my head.

One of the toughest days was coming home and digging through the mail to find his college diploma had arrived about a month after he passed.

How could I have missed the signs?

And when the signs came, how come I failed to act or just didn't know what to do help the situation?

After the memorial service, we all struggled to adjust to the new normal.

Yes, we heard from our grief counselors, our pastor, family and friends that he would always be in our hearts. But the grief counselor or anyone else did not have to walk by a quiet, empty room in our house where he used to sleep.

Or look at an empty seat where he used to eat dinner. Or hear the sounds of rubber wheels on concrete from the skateboard some kid in the neighborhood was riding, thinking he was home from school.

It was probably worse for Ann and the boys. I worried about Amani going back to school in Tempe. Thankfully he had the support of his then girlfriend and network of friends and family. How could a 20-year old concentrate on school after having to bury his Kuya?

As kids they always hung out together and like most siblings, you find other interests and new friends to hang out with, as you get older.

But Amani always looked up to Avery because he set the bar high for what we expected out of the boys and Amani worked hard to meet and exceed those goals. Avery didn't always say a lot, but he was proud that Amani tried so hard to live up to the legacy he was leaving.

Then there was Aden. The little brother or "scrub" as Avery called him. In so many ways, Avery was the perfect big brother for Aden because they were both quiet and did their work without any fanfare.

It was tough for Aden to walk past Avery's empty room and not be able to stop in ask questions about algorithms for the rubiks cube or about a video game.

Of course, nothing is worse than a mother grieving and looking for answers. Ann first blamed herself for not acting more quickly. Then she blamed me one day, it was for being too hard on the boys.

Why did I have to push Avery into a professional career?

The next day I wasn't hard enough. Back and forth it went. The therapist said it was normal for the grieving parents to want to assign blame. I have to admit it was tough for me to hear.

Through it all, I did my best to stay strong for my family.

But I was struggling myself inside. It was almost like I was on autopilot. After taking a few weeks, I went back to work in my consulting firm, trying my best to hide the emotional toll of what had happened from friends, colleagues and clients.

I would go to meetings and almost like clockwork; I would have to excuse myself after an hour.

I would go to my car, stick the key in the ignition and before I could turn the switch, I would just start crying. This went on for weeks.

Then I got an unexpected email from a high school classmate.

CHAPTER 6

Friend Request

Faith consists in believing when it is beyond the power of reason to believe. It is not enough that a thing be possible for it to be believed.

- Voltaire

October 1, 2017, will forever be remembered by those of us who live in Southern Nevada for the tragic shooting on the Las Vegas Strip now known as the 1 October shooting that claimed 59 lives and injured many more.

The largest mass shooting in the United States led to an outpouring of support from around the world and the trending hashtag: #VegasStrong.

About 24 hours later, I would remember that time frame for another reason:

Reconnecting with a friend from high school, Jeanette Lee.

I got a text from Amani early the morning of October 1, asking if I had seen the news. I turned on the television to flashing Breaking News reports that seem to be the norm in the post 911 era. He was heading back to Tempe from Los Angeles, so at least I knew he was not at the concert or near the Strip.

In 2001, I was promoted to a corporate communications director position and our offices were in one of the towers at Mandalay Bay Hotel and Casino, where the shooter fired his deadly shots.

The next day as I was following the events online, checking in on colleagues and standing by to assist clients with crisis communications, I notice an email in my inbox. It was a request to connect on the social media site LinkedIn from Jeanette Lee, tennis teammate of mine at Inglewood.

I immediately remembered her as a smart, outgoing and supportive friend, who wanted to be a doctor. So, it was no surprise that her profile read: Dr. Jeanette Lee.

The invite included a brief message:

Hello there! Remember me, Jeanette Lee? OMG, I was going through Inglewood High School stuff as I was cleaning up a bunch of boxes from my parents home ... just wanted to say "hi."

Jeanette and I played on the tennis team together, so of course, I remembered her. Besides, there were not many Asian students at our school except her and her brother Daniel, now a medical doctor.

I accepted the invite and wrote back:

"Wow, is this really Jeanette Lee?! One of my favorite tennis doubles partners from high school? It's great to hear from you. How is life treating you, your parents, Daniel?"

We didn't have the best players, team or program, but we had a cool, diverse group and enjoyed being around each other for practice and matches.

Jeanette and I lost touch after high school with college and life getting in the way. To the best of our recollection, it had been over 30 years since we had last seen or spoken. We had lots to catch up on. But our reunion would have to wait.

I used to work on the Strip and at Mandalay Bay, so The 1 October shooting was still fresh on everyone's mind. So we exchanged contact information and agreed it was not a good time for a full-on reunion, but that we would keep in touch. When things settled down, maybe we could jump on a call.

We exchanged several messages over the next few days. She sent a picture of her with her two boys on a family vacation in Italy.

I sent her a photo with the boys at Top Golf on Father's Day. Around Friday of that week, we agreed that things had calmed down enough to speak by phone.

When the call came through, I recognized the voice right away. And almost immediately, we started our telephonic class reunion.

She told me about her father passing away a few years earlier and the challenge of selling the house in LA and taking care of her mom. As much as I had been through, I could tell she was still coping with the loss of her father.

For a brief moment, it was a relief not to talk about the loss that I had suffered. I figured it would eventually come up.

The conversation shifted away from family to our friends. Do you remember so and so? The normal conversation you would have with someone you had not spoken with in over three decades!

We were on the phone for about an hour and it was getting late. Dr. Lee had been competing in marathons for years. Aside from tennis, she played volleyball in high school, so it was no surprise that she remained active. She needed to rest up for an event that weekend.

I had a flag football game with Aden the next morning. Before we hung up, I remember saying something like: *"the next time talk I need to tell you something about one of my boys."*

I was not more specific. I recall her response was something like: *"Yes, I feel we have some unfinished business."*

It seemed like an odd comment at the time or maybe I just misremembered, but it was late and I would have to wait until the next day to find out what it all meant.

On Saturday afternoon, Aden and I made it back from flag football and were relaxing in the family room watching college football games. My cell phone rang and it was Dr. Lee.

I answered: "What's up Doc?" She sounded nervous and unsure.

I told her to hold on for second while I moved into the next room.

"Reggie, I feel like I was supposed to call you. It's something about one of your boys – they are either hurt or ... "

Before I could hear another word from Dr. Lee, the voice on the other end of the phone changed and so did the emotion.

"I'm so sorry, I'm so sorry, do you forgive me?" The voice on the other end of the phone said through tears.

I wasn't 100 percent certain, but in my heart, I knew it was Avery. I felt his energy.

I responded, *"Of course I forgive you. I miss you. We do. We miss and love you. Continue your journey."*

Both of my parents were from the South and grew up in Louisiana. My dad from Shreveport and my mom Monroe - church on Sunday was a part of my childhood. However, I would not call myself overly religious.

That said, I could feel a spiritual connection happening during the call. It's the only way I can explain my responses and saying what I said.

I knew in my heart I was talking to my son.

As we both were fighting back emotions, I said to Dr. Lee:

"I really don't know what just happened."

I recall her response was something like:

"Reggie, this is what I've been trying to tell you. I have this gift ... had it my whole life ... your son found me to give you a message."

Before I could say anything, Avery came back.

"I'm so sorry, I'm so sorry, please forgive me."

I said, *"Yes son, I ... we forgive you. Do you want to say anything to your brothers?"* I asked.

He said, *"I'm so sorry I let them down. I'm so sorry I let them down,"* and I quickly told him it was *"Okay, they understand. You will always be their big brother and they miss their Kuya."*

Dr. Lee came back and waited for a minute to see if Avery might come back again. She then took the next few minutes to explain what happened:

"Avery's spirit needed forgiveness so he could continue his journey. He was feeling remorseful for the pain he had caused the family, friends and knew were grieving and in pain."

Although I could not fully process what had just happened, I immediately felt a sense of relief.

It was relief in knowing that my son was okay and no longer in pain. I didn't know how, but I felt his energy and emotion through the phone.

Still, part of me was skeptical. Maybe it was my journalism training where everything is to be questioned to make sense of the story. So I called my sister Stephanie.

"Steph, do you remember Jeanette Lee from the tennis team?" She said, "Yeah boo, why?"

Have you heard from her recently? Is there any way she would know about what happened to Avery?"

"No Reg. I have not seen or talked to her," she replied.

In tears, I told my sister what happened on the call with Jeanette.

Instead of questioning what I told her, Stephanie went on to tell share a similar spiritual experience she had after my father passed away.

Indirectly, reconnecting with Dr. Lee gave my grief purpose. Without her delivering the message from Avery, I would not have been able to talk to my son and be able to share his request for forgiveness with Ann, the boys, our family, and friends.

Despite the painful loss of Avery, I had regained a friend for life and an ally in my fight against depression.

And while I did not know at the time why Dr. Lee was chosen to help deliver this message, I had faith and trusted in our friendship. As we would later find out, Dr. Lee's mission was not done.

A note of condolence from a colleague or co-worker. The cajoling embrace of a family member. A shoulder to cry on from a good friend. The support of your faith community.

Anyone going through the grieving process will find solace wherever you can get it. One day at a time is the motto. The reality is it takes as long as it needs to take. Everyone heals differently.

For me, my healing process was aided by the spiritual world.

CHAPTER 7

We'll Take It From Here

*"I really know how it feels to be stressed out, stressed out.
When you're face to face with your adversity ... We're going
to make this thing work out eventually."*

- Tribe Called Quest

My first job out of college was as a reporter at the Reno Gazette-Journal. I was the full-time prep editor, covering high school sports. I was also a general assignment reporter, meaning that sometimes I was asked to fill in on other beats or develop my own or enterprise stories.

Soon after Avery passed away, I acted on my instinct to find out what happened to my son and figure out a way to help other people going through the same thing he had.

How does a smart, athletic outgoing young person with all the love and support from family and friends you could have and a whole life seemingly in front of him be stressed out?

More importantly, what was depression and what were the causes?

The experience with Dr. Lee helped provide the healing and closure I needed to search for answers.

You hear or read about so many cases where someone commits suicide and leaves very few clues to help family and friends understand the reasons why.

I told Ann, the boys, a few family members and close friends about the call with Dr. Lee. I reluctantly told the therapists, as I did not want them to invalidate my spiritual experience and the role it had in my healing.

I figured they probably thought I was dreaming or imagined it happening. All I knew or cared about was the peace I had gained and the message of forgiveness.

At one point, Ann asked me how much I paid Dr. Lee to speak with Avery.

Rather than trying to explain what I still fully didn't understand, I focused on the message and not the messenger.

Perhaps more importantly, the Jeanette I remembered had always been a good person, teammate and friend. I recalled her from high school as always looking out for others.

With my healing process underway, the opportunity to reconnect with Jeanette would come sooner than I expected.

A few weeks had passed since we talked then one day I get a call. She was coming to Las Vegas for the Rock N Roll Marathon, which occurred the first week or second week of November. She was an avid runner and competed in marathons all over the country.

But this trip was different. *"I'm not coming to run,"* she said. *"Avery is sending me on a mission."*

According to Dr. Lee, Avery knew certain people were still grieving, including his brother Aden. So she asked me to coordinate a meeting with his close friends in The Squad, a group of classmates and co-workers from college that often hung out together on weekends and took "Squadcations" on hiking and camping trips.

And he needed to see Aden.

So I arranged a meeting with about six of his friends at UNLV, including one who was having a particularly hard time with her grief.

I met Dr. Lee at the airport in Las Vegas on Friday of the Rock and Roll Marathon. She had plans to meet up with some friends from her running group later, but the mission was first.

Because we had not seen each other in close to 30 years, I had to look at the photo of her with her boys to remember what she looked like. We met at passenger pick up, exchanged a quick hello and hug and immediately jumped in the car and headed over to UNLV.

There was no time to waste.

We parked at the school and headed to the campus recreational center. One of his friends was there, so we met with her in a private room. Dr. Lee told me she didn't know what was going to happen, but told me to bring tissue.

Dr. Lee asked her a few questions about how she was feeling. Then she became more direct. "Have you thought about suicide," The response was "Yes".

How recent, Dr. Lee asked. "Within the last 10 days, the response came."

It turns out Avery was right. Tears flowed from his friend and Dr. Lee as I sat and watched fighting back emotions. Then he came. He spoke to her through Dr. Lee and told her she had a long life ahead of her. She asked if he knew about the tattoo she just got. He said yes, it's under your heart and amazing.

They both stood up and hugged and I pulled out the tissue from my backpack, as the tears were flowing from all four of us.

Later on, we met with his other friends on the grass outside the pool area. Although Avery did not come to speak to his friends, he used Dr. Lee and me to deliver his message: he was sorry he left his friends this way and was remorseful. He needed their forgiveness.

The next day on Saturday, we met up at Aden's flag football game. By now Dr. Lee had checked into her room and rented a car. So she drove for a run near Hoover Dam to clear her head and get ready to meet with Aden.

She arrived at the football field in Henderson and met him during the game on the sidelines. He knew why Dr. Lee was there but didn't know what was going to happen or how.

None of us did.

After the game, we drove to pick up Subway sandwiches and headed over to Foothill High School. Dr. Lee said we needed to be in a space that was familiar to both Aden and Avery.

We sat down on the grass near the tennis courts, not far from the football field where Avery played tennis and ran track. A few bites into our food, Dr. Lee asked Aden how he was doing and if he missed his brother.

Fighting back tears, Aden said he was ok and yes, he did miss him. Then Avery came. He told his brother he was sorry he could not be there for him and needed his forgiveness.

Dr. Lee's visit and mission were complete. Avery needed to deliver a message to his friends and brother. Amani was at school and in a good space. Ann was healing at her own pace, but Avery would be keeping an eye on her and would reach out to her when she was ready.

For me, my mission was just beginning.

Looking back, he had left many clues and information behind. As the depression began to take over his life, Avery began to isolate himself and withdrew from meeting up with friends and social media. However, his devices contained numerous text messages and chats offering detailed conversations he had with friends.

I called them pieces to a puzzle. He knew he was depressed. He tried to do something to help himself, but this was one situation he couldn't fix by himself.

When I got his phone back from the Las Vegas Metro Police Department, his Spotify app opened up to a Linkin Park song, "In the end." I knew the song but was not that familiar with the lyrics.

The song talked about how hard this person tried ... but in the end, it didn't matter. When I watched the video, the imagery matched the darkness of the song. I also recognized the writer. His name was Chester Bennington, co-lead singer of Linkin Park.

As I was looking at Avery's social media, someone had posted on his timeline an article about Bennington, who had just committed suicide. Avery LIKED it.

A few weeks after Avery passed, UNLV announced that it had increased tuition for the 2017 Fall Semester by $25 to help increase support staff for mental health counselors. Why? The average wait for a student needing an appointment was 4-6 weeks.

Then a few weeks later, UCLA announced for the first time, that it would be providing free mental health screenings for all incoming freshman and transfer students. UCLA is perennially one of the most difficult schools to get into and even more difficult after you get in. A place filled with stressed-out students trying to maintain academic progress.

What was it about depression? Avery was admired by everyone in our family for everything he accomplished in school and sports. He was respected by his peers for his brains, work ethic, and his competitive but friendly nature.

Again, I kept coming back to the same question: *"Why would a kid who seemingly had a bright future and whole life ahead of him to choose to end it at 22?"*

One friend shared a Ted Talks Video that Avery had sent him a few weeks before he passed. On the video, there was a guy talking about his depression, describing his attempted suicide on a freeway overpass.

Halfway through the video, the speaker compared his stress to driving 100 miles per hour and slamming on the breaks. Avery texted his friend that was how he felt with graduation and suddenly having to slow down.

So, why wasn't mental health and depression higher on my list?

In order to prevent what happened to Avery from happening to another family, I had to educate myself on the problem.

As Avery used to say, "how can you solve a problem if you don't know one exists?

CHAPTER 8

13 Things You Should Know About Depression

We cannot afford to forget any experience, not even the most painful.

- Dag Hammarksjold

In some strange way, we have found purpose and calm in our grief.

It started with doing something to honor Avery's memory. So in 2018, we launched the Avery Burton Excellence in Academics and Sports Scholarship at his alma mater Foothill High School.

Writing this book was not only therapeutic, but opening up I hoped to lend my voice to an important conversation.

In 2019, we will be forming and launching The Avery Burton Foundation, which will serve as a resource for advocacy and fundraising in support of issues related to mental health and depression.

Finally, there are many lessons learned and more to come. Here are a few that I hope help inspire everyone to keep the conversation going.

Depression Does Not Discriminate. Depression does not care if you are white, black, Latino or Asian. It does not care if you are poor or rich. Depression does not care about socioeconomic status.

Depression does not care if you come from a nuclear family with two parents or a single parent home. Depression does not care about gender. Depression does not care if you are an adult or a teenager. Basically, depression can affect anyone.

Start by having a conversation. Let's make it less "awkward" to discuss mental health and depression with a child or loved one. Help someone dealing with stress find "their voice" by listening and encouraging the person to get professional help.

Homesickness. I have been to two college freshman orientations. I can tell you everything you need to know about the Freshman 15, where students can go to get condoms on campus and homesickness. But I don't recall much time spent on depression or what happens if your student has a depressive episode. Make sure you know who to call and what resources are available.

"There's Nobody to Blame". Were we too hard? Not hard enough? Did we push him into a professional career and add to much pressure? The first step towards healing is to forgive yourself for what you think you did or didn't do.

Don't be afraid to ask. When someone is depressed, they don't hear the words of encouragement. Be direct: "Have you been thinking about suicide?" Experts say it won't make the situation worse if the person is thinking about it.

Switch things up. Instead of asking how are they doing, ask how are you *feeling*?

Be aware of online habits. If you share a Netflix account and 13 Reasons Why is in the queue or has been recently streamed, ask why they watched it or planned to.

Removing the Stigma. Let's change the way we talk about depression. There is nothing wrong with being on anti-depressants or seeing a therapist.

JOMO. Social media use can lead to unhealthy habits. Instead of fretting over The Fear of Missing Out, learn the Joy of Missing Out.

See something, say something. If your friend or someone you know is struggling emotionally, let the parents know. It's not snitching or violating trust. It's being a good friend

Communication. Like the cliché in real estate, it's communication, communication, and communication.

Alcohol. It's a depressant, so drinking while you are depressed will only make things worse, not better.

Self-medication. Cannabis is legal for adults over 21 in 10 states; medical marijuana is legal in 33 states. If you are going to use it to treat anxiety or depression, get professional advice on what works or doesn't work.

The importance of sleep. Your body uses sleep to replenish your body and mind. When you are under stress and or depressed, your subconscious mind begins to take over and limits your ability to think rationally and unable to distinguish suicidal thoughts from reality. It's important for any healthy person to get at least 7 hours of sleep, even more, important for someone experiencing a depressive episode.

Instead of running from my grief, I chose to embrace it. In the spirit of the cliché, life gave me lemons, so I'm making lemonade. I look forward to sharing this story with as many people as possible as an advocate for mental health and depression outreach and awareness. Most importantly, I hope to inspire and motivate people to live with passion and purpose. For inspiration, I need not look any further than a quote Avery had on the profile of his Facebook page:

> "I don't have weekdays in my calendar, only strong days." – Avery Burton

> If you or someone you know is struggling to find "their voice", call 1-800-273-TALK.

According to the Foundation for Suicide Prevention (AFSP), "the important issue is that most suicides are preventable, partly because most people who die by suicide suffer from the serious but very treatable disorder, clinical depression."

First, know the facts. Psychiatric disorders: More than 90 percent of people who kill themselves are suffering from one or more psychiatric disorders in particular:

- Bipolar depression
- Alcohol abuse and dependence
- Schizophrenia
- Post Traumatic Stress Disorder (PTSD)
- Eating disorders
- Personality disorders

The core symptoms of major depression are a "down" or depressed mood most of the day or a loss of interest or pleasure in activities that were previously enjoyed for at least two weeks, as well as:

- Changes in sleeping patterns
- Change in appetite or weight
- Intense anxiety, agitation restlessness or being slowed down
- Fatigue or loss of energy
- Decreased concentration, indecisiveness or poorer memory
- Feelings of hopelessness, worthlessness, self-reproach or excessive or inappropriate guilt
- Recurrent thoughts of death or suicide

If you recognize any of the symptoms displayed by a loved one, take it seriously. Some of the Do's include:

- If he/she is depressed, don't be afraid to ask whether he/she is considering suicide, or if he/she has a particular plan or method.
- Let them know you are concerned
- Ask if they have a therapist and are taking medication

Do not attempt to argue someone out of suicide. Rather, let the person know you care, that he/she is not alone, those suicidal feelings are temporary and that depression can be treated. Avoid the temptation to say," You have so much to live for," or "Your suicide will hurt your family."

If you are unclear on what to do, visit www.AFSP.org.

While I will leave suicide prevention to the professionals, my family and I are dedicating the rest of our lives to outreach and advocacy about mental health and depression. We and Avery don't want another family to go through what we had to endure unnecessarily.

First, I would start with how we talk about depression.

As much as the support from family and friends helped our healing process, it was frustrating to hear comments questioning Avery's "relationship with God" or his "Faith" as if to suggest Avery's struggle with depression was some sort of "Good vs. Evil" battle.

We don't demonize someone with Cancer this way. We shouldn't treat mental health or suicidal thoughts as something someone chooses to have. Other suggestions:

Instead of comforting our friends and loved ones who are showing signs of struggling by asking how they are doing, ask "how are you feeling"?

It's time we flip the script. It's time for real conversations about mental health and depression.

That's why I decided to write this book. I didn't want another parent or family to experience the pain we did. By sharing this experience, I wanted to help inspire people to take action.

We wanted to memorialize Avery, so we the first thing we did was start a scholarship in his name. In 2018, with the help of the Public Education Foundation, a non-profit organization in Las Vegas, we started the Avery Burton Excellence in Sports and Academics Scholarship at Foothill High School.

Thanks to the generous support of family and friends, we were able to award a $1,000 scholarship to an FHS graduate attending the

University of Nevada, Reno. The criteria included the student writing an essay about dealing with and overcoming adversity.

In the future, we hope to open it up to students from Las Vegas area and beyond.

There are plans for a nonprofit organization that will help people and families dealing with depression find resources and fundraising events to raise money for the scholarship.

****

CHAPTER 9

Avery Strong

Who is Avery Rashawn Burton?

He was smart, funny, a hard worker and amazing athlete. He was offered a Presidential Scholarship to Johnson and Wales University, but he was born to be a Rebel – A UNLV Rebel.

Avery lived life to the fullest. He worked two jobs pretty much all through college. I made sure they were on campus jobs, so that he could stay focused, with no excuse not to hit the library after school

Was he perfect? Nope. He could be a bit stubborn and he didn't have much time to engage in small talk. He was too busy doing life.

In many ways, he was your typical 22-year old that still needed to be told to clean his room when he was home.

But he loved spending time with family on vacation and his friends at school and on the weekends.

He also enjoyed the outdoors and was a bit of a daredevil, including cliff diving at Nelson's Landing.

He posted a photo to his social media of him after a hike with his backpack gear on, looking at a canyon in the distance. The caption read:

"Life is about pushing outside of your comfort zone."

He was a leader and served as an officer in a pre-therapy fraternity, but not a nerd. He wrestled and practiced jujitsu with his friends every Sunday night.

I told him he would fit in anywhere, because of his approach to life I called "Intellectual Brutality" a nickname used by the Stanford football team.

He reminded me of this on a regular basis.

He was extremely disciplined with his diet, ate clean most of the time except for his juicy gummy bears, which were his pre and post workout snack.

He loved to prepare his own meals for the day. Athletes use the term Meal Prep. His go-to meal was usually chicken breast, rice, black beans with siracha sauce.

Ann would buy packages of chicken on sale, cut up and put the chicken in foil and into the freezer. Avery would cook the food in the morning or beginning of the week depending on how much time he had or his schedule and pack his lunch for the day.

There was the time he started getting this nutrition drink delivered to the house. I would ask him what it was and responded, *"it's Soylant"* as if I was supposed to know.

"What's that?" I would ask.

"It's the future of food," he would smile as he grabbed a bottle and would head off to school.

I used to tell him that if PT school and becoming a doctor didn't work out, he could become an underwear model.

The morning was our time to talk and catch up before school and work. So I would ask him about current events or politics, which he could care less about.

One day I asked him, so have you seen Oprah's new movie? He said no, *"What's it about"*?

In my proud father about to educate my son's voice, *"I said it's about Henryetta Lacks, a black woman whose cells were stolen by John's Hopkins and she became the mother of biomedicine ..."* I started.

Avery grabs his backpack and is about to leave for school, turns around retrieves a book from his room and hands it to me.

He said, *"Oh you mean they made a movie out of this book. You can keep it."*

He smiled, grabbed a Soylant and headed out the door to school.

Intellectual Brutality.

If Avery were here, what would he want us to know?

What would he say?

- He would tell you he made a unilateral decision. Nobody did anything to him or said anything to him.

He knew he was depressed and could not see things getting better with or without treatment or medication. He was smart and knew he could manipulate any therapist into thinking he was fine. Most of all, he doesn't want his choice to be yours or mine.

- He would say that he's sorry and extremely remorseful for the pain he caused.

Although he made a decision to end the pain he was feeling, he didn't realize the commotion him not being around would cause his family and friends

- Being depressed doesn't define who you are.

He wants people, especially boys and young men, to know it's okay to not feel okay. To not keep all your feelings bottled up inside. Find ways to express yourself.

- Talking about depression and mental health can be awkward

the stigma around talking about mental health and ometimes parents, friends and loved ones have to make ve.

- It's hard when you don't have a voice.

If you have trouble expressing yourself, find another way. Write it down. Get outdoors. Exercise. Paint or draw. Figure out whatever works for you.

Although no longer here in the physical sense, Avery left his mark and his words.

The quote on the profile page of his Facebook page is a reminder to us all:

> "I don't have weekdays in my calendar – only strong days." – Avery Burton

AFTERWARD

Before I started writing this book, I got the opportunity to speak at Foothill High School in Henderson during Senior Awards Night. Both Avery and Amani graduated from FHS, Avery in 2013 and Amani in 2017. So I was familiar with the school. It's a big night for the administration, faculty, students and of course, the proud parents.

I was there to present the first Avery Burton Memorial Scholarship. The family came up with the idea as a way to honor his memory and recognize students overcoming adversity.

As I walked into the nicely decorated auditorium adorned with blue and gold balloons, I was immediately overcome with emotion. I was wearing a blue suit, white dress shirt with a blue and gold tie. Man, Avery loved that tie. On one of his Instagram posts from his senior awards night, he called me Mr. Falcon, the name of the blue and gold school mascot. As I made my way into the auditorium past the student ushers, I started fixing my tie, but I really was trying to calm my nerves and was looking for some help from Avery.

As I walked onto the stage to find my seat, my emotions were starting to take over. I was a mess. I made eye contact with one of the administrators. It was Principal Lisa Burkhead. She knew I was struggling and came over. She showed me my seat and gave me a look that said, "I'm here if you need me" and left me alone.

My presentation was at the end of the ceremony. So I had some to time to gather myself. As I sat and listened to the other speakers, I asked Avery to help me stay strong. I immediately started to feel a sense of calm. It had to be Avery. Then it was my turn. I strolled up to the podium and gave the following remarks:

"THANK YOU TO PRINCIPAL BURKHEAD AND THE COUNSELING STAFF HERE AT FOOTHILL HIGH SCHOOL FOR THE INVITATION.

I WAS ASKED TO BE HERE AND PRESENT THE FIRST AVERY BURTON MEMORIAL SCHOLARSHIP, NAMED AFTER MY SON. BEFORE I DO THAT, ALLOW ME TO TAKE A MOMENT TO SHARE SOME BACKGROUND WITH YOU.

A LITTLE OVER 4 YEARS AGO, MY FAMILY AND I SAT IN THE AUDIENCE TO CELEBRATE AVERY'S ACCOMPLISHMENTS AS A STUDENT ATHLETE. HE GRADUATED WITH HIGH HONORS AND WAS A THREE SPORTS ATHLETE IN TENNIS, WRESTLING AND TRACK, HELPING SET THE SCHOOL RECORD IN THE 4X200 RELAY HIS SENIOR YEAR.

IN 2017 AVERY GRADUATED FROM UNLV CUM LAUDE, WITH A DEGREE IN KINESIOLOGICAL SCIENCES. HIS EXCEPTIONAL LEADERSHIP EARNED HIM RESPECT FROM HIS PROFESSORS, COLLEAGUES AT WORK AND PEERS. HE PASSED THE GRE ON HIS FIRST TRY AND WAS SET TO APPLY TO THE UNLV SCHOOL OF PHYSICAL THERAPY. HE WANTED TO BE A PHYSICAL THERAPIST SO HE COULD HELP PEOPLE.

HE NEVER GOT THAT CHANCE. ON AUGUST 6, 2017, AVERY LOST HIS LIFE TO A DEPRESSIVE EPISODE. HE WAS 22. HE WAS ALSO PART OF A DISTURBING STATISTIC WE KNEW NOTHING ABOUT: ACCORDING TO PUBLISHED STUDIES, **1 IN 4 COLLEGE STUDENTS SUFFERS FROM DEPRESSION.**

DURING THIS DIFFICULT TIME, OUR FAMILY DECIDED WE WANTED TO HONOR AVERY'S MEMORY WHILE AT THE SAME TIME CREATE AWARENESS FOR MENTAL HEALTH AND DEPRESSION.

THANKS TO FAMILY, FRIENDS AND GENEROUS DONORS, WE SET UP THE FIRST ANNUAL AVERY BURTON **EXCELLENCE**

IN ACADEMICS AND SPORTS MEMORIAL SCHOLARSHIP, WHERE WE ASK STUDENTS TO "EXPLAIN A SITUATION WHERE YOU HAD TO OVERCOME AN ADVERSITY."

SO, ON BEHALF OF OUR FAMILY WE ARE PROUD TO PRESENT THE FIRST SCHOLARSHIP TO .... **Zachary Williams"**

I shook the student's hand as he came up on stage and left right after handing out the $1,000 dollar scholarship. As I made my way from the stage, I could hear the applause from the students and parents. I started heading towards the back of the room and immediately saw Tiff, a member of The Squad – a small close-knit group of Avery's friends he met at UNLV. They spent time with Avery at school and on Squadcations, hiking and camping trips everywhere from Zion to Venice Beach. A few of them were there to support me. I asked how I did, and she said you were great.

Ann and Aden were also there. Amani was in Tempe finishing up his junior at Barrett, The Honors College at Arizona State University. As we began to exit the auditorium through the back, one of Amani's FHS teachers, Mr. Smith came over to me. He thanked me and said he was proud of Amani and thanked us for setting up the scholarship.

But what he told after that left an impression on me: "Mr. Burton, I was surrounded by a bunch of teachers standing in the back of the auditorium. There was not a dry eye in the room where we were standing."

That's when it dawned on me. I needed to use my platform to help create awareness for mental health and depression, as well as suicide. Teachers are on the front lines dealing with students constantly dealing with stress in their lives. Writing a book on my personal experiences healing after Avery's death was natural. I was a former journalist and produce tons of press releases and written pieces content for clients in my boutique social media and public relations firm. I had always loved writing.

I also had given numerous public speeches and talks throughout my corporate career working in the NFL as a public relations specialist for the San Diego Chargers and in corporate communications for two casino gaming companies based in Las Vegas – Mandalay Resort Group and MGM Mirage.

As we moved outside in the quad area of campus to meet up with other members of the Squad and catch up over taking out pizza, it was then I decided that public speaking to schools would be part of my effort to help reduce the odds of what happened to Avery to happening to other students and their families.

ACKNOWLEDGMENTS

The contents of this book are based on my personal story of healing after losing my son to depression. First, I need to thank my wife Ann, the patriarch of our family for helping me stay strong for our boys, Amani and Aden. I appreciate their understanding and encouragement for all the times when it might have seemed I was not present while working. I love you, Team Burton.

Special gratitude goes out to all the friends and family who contributed to my healing process with well wishes or dropping off a plate of food. Your encouragement reaffirmed my faith in community and helped fuel my drive to start and finish this book. Too many people to list individually, but you know who you are. Lil Mike – Thank you for taking the drone photo after the memorial – We Are Family. A special note to the Manabat and Burton Family, I hope this book fills you with lessons of love, hope and healing in your time of need. We love you all.

Thanks to The staff at the Public Education Foundation, which helped us launch the Avery Burton Excellence in Academics and Sports Scholarship with an assist from PEF Board Member and my longtime colleague and dear friend, Rose McKinney-James. Also, want thank those who graciously donated to the scholarship and served as volunteers on the scholarship review committee. Special thanks to Jonathan Galaviz, Ken Heck, two of my colleagues from The Economic Club of Las Vegas, where I serve as a volunteer officer. Howard Stutz, Joe Ayson and too many others to list, but you know who you are. Efrain Rene, George McCabe and all the guys from Sunday Basketball – thank you for your support.

So many of Avery's friends were instrumental in helping provide content, inspiration and support. He was a three-sport athlete in high school, so he had a diverse, fun group to hang out with. The wrestlers, the track and field teams and the tennis players. Our Vanderburg Elementary, Bob Miller Middle School and Foothill High School, the entire Henderson community. Again, too many to list, but you know who you are. A special note to the Squad – his friends from college at UNLV. He spent many hours with them in class, at work as a lifeguard and physical trainer at UNLV or hanging out.

Sincere appreciation to our faith community, who we leaned on heavily. Especially Father Dan and the staff at St. Thomas More. Special thanks to Foothill High School Principal Lisa Burkhead and administration for your support of the scholarship.

Last but not least, Dr. Jeanette Lee. My tennis teammate from Inglewood High School. Thank you for sharing your gift with me. We had some fun battles on those raggedy courts at IHS and formed a life long bond in the process. Now we have another battle on our hands and a formidable opponent – depression. A distinguished alumnae and a better person. Your friendship then and now means the world to me.

R. Avery Burton is the owner of RB Group Public Relations, an author and entrepreneur. His is president of the Avery Burton Foundation, a non-profit dedicated to mental health outreach and advocacy. Proceeds from book sales will go towards the Avery Burton Excellence in Academics and Athletics Scholarship. He lives in Henderson, NV with his family.

Visit www.thisisdepressionthebook.com or www.reggieburton.com for more information.

CPSIA information can be obtained
at www.ICGtesting.com
Printed in the USA
FSHW011404021019
62612FS